XANTH Graphic Novel Vol. 1

RETURN to CENTAUR

(or: What Kind of Foal Am I?)

Being the First Part of the Adaptation of "Isle of View" by Piers Anthony

for the Graphic Novel:
Script by Richard Pini
Art by Dennis Fujitake
Colors by Gary Kato

Father Tree Press · Poughkeepsie NY · 1990

Xanth Graphic Novel Vol. 1:
Return to Centaur

Xanth Graphic Novel #1: Return to Centaur is the first part of a licensed adaptation of the prose novel **Isle of View** by Piers Anthony, and published in paperback by Avon Books.

Published by Father Tree Press
    Warp Graphics, Inc., 5 Reno Road, Poughkeepsie NY 12603

ISBN: 0-936862-20-7

First Printing: July 1990

0 9 8 7 6 5 4 3 2 1

Printed in the United States of America

Introduction
by Piers Anthony

In FeBlueberry 1989 I received a letter from the mother of Jenny, a twelve year old girl who was in a months-long coma as the result of being hit by a drunk driver. She asked me to write to Jenny, and perhaps name a character in a Xanth novel after her, as Xanth was her favorite fantasy series. I did write, and my letter was read to Jenny, and it did bring her out of her coma. Unfortunately she remained almost completely paralyzed, not even able to talk. So I continued to write to her and to discuss things that I hoped would be of interest to her.

Among these things was Elfquest, another of Jenny's favorites. I discovered that a regular Xanth Elf would not do for the character I needed, because Xanth elves are tied too closely to their Elf Elms. An elf from the World of Two Moons, however, would work well. So, with the permission of the Elfquest folk, I brought Jenny Elf to Xanth. She thus became of composite of three: Xanth, Elfquest, and the original Jenny herself, and had her effect on the ongoing adventure. I had known that Che Centaur would be lost, and that Prince Dolph would have to choose which fiancee to marry, but I hadn't realized that this new character would be interacting with both of these stories and helping to unify them. Jenny Elf looks like Jenny of Mundania, except for the ears and hands and the wheelchair, and her cat Sammy is unchanged except that his magic works better in Xanth.

As it happened, the Xanth folk and the Elfquest folk had been flirting with the notion of a liaison for about six years. No point in rushing things, after all. Now, with Jenny as the catalyst, we got serious. Here was the perfect novel for a mergence: it already had elements of both. An elf of the World of Two Moons in

Xanth. So we—Richard Pini, Piers Anthony, and Jenny—met at a science fiction convention in Virginia, Sci-Con 11, in NoRemember 1989, and—well, I forget exactly what happened, for some reason, but this is the result: the graphic edition of Xanth #13, *Isle of View*. Jenny had her influence not only in Xanth, but in the dreary Mundane world of books and contracts, making it slightly less dull that it used to be.

Meanwhile, Richard and I showed Jenny around the convention. Her injuries are such that she is unable to remain sitting in the wheelchair long, and must lie down soon to rest. When she is "up" she is strapped in the chair. She can laugh, but can't move her mouth well enough for normal speech, so uses hand signals with her functional hand to spell out words, slowly. She is still recovering, and making gains, but progress is glacial. Despite this, she is a cheerful girl, smiling often and making a sign of a blown kiss for "Thank you." As this graphic novel is published, she is on the verge of fourteen, a young lady, and is attending a school for those with extensive disabilities. Don't worry, Jenny Elf will catch up in due course!

It is nice to have things work out, and I hope you enjoy this adaptation, but I regret that a tragedy is at the heart of it. If there is anything further to be gained from this, let it be this: make sure that you, the reader, never contribute to a similar tragedy. Don't drink and drive. If you're too young to drive yet, keep this resolution in mind for the time when you are old enough. We don't live in a fantasy realm, but in a world of sometimes brutal realities; let's not make it even worse. Jenny will thank you.

X O X O X

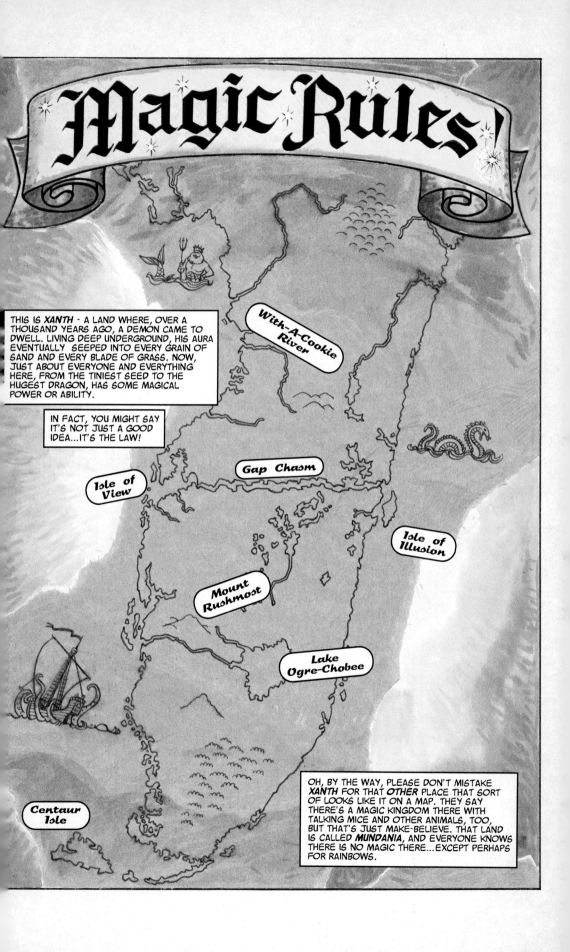

Magic Rules!

THIS IS *XANTH* - A LAND WHERE, OVER A THOUSAND YEARS AGO, A DEMON CAME TO DWELL. LIVING DEEP UNDERGROUND, HIS AURA EVENTUALLY SEEPED INTO EVERY GRAIN OF SAND AND EVERY BLADE OF GRASS. NOW, JUST ABOUT EVERYONE AND EVERYTHING HERE, FROM THE TINIEST SEED TO THE HUGEST DRAGON, HAS SOME MAGICAL POWER OR ABILITY.

IN FACT, YOU MIGHT SAY IT'S NOT JUST A GOOD IDEA...IT'S THE LAW!

With-A-Cookie River

Gap Chasm

Isle of View

Isle of Illusion

Mount Rushmost

Lake Ogre-Chobee

Centaur Isle

OH, BY THE WAY, PLEASE DON'T MISTAKE *XANTH* FOR THAT *OTHER* PLACE THAT SORT OF LOOKS LIKE IT ON A MAP. THEY SAY THERE'S A MAGIC KINGDOM THERE WITH TALKING MICE AND OTHER ANIMALS, TOO, BUT THAT'S JUST MAKE-BELIEVE. THAT LAND IS CALLED *MUNDANIA*, AND EVERYONE KNOWS THERE IS NO MAGIC THERE...EXCEPT PERHAPS FOR RAINBOWS.

THEN THERE ARE ALL THE VARIETIES OF *MONSTERS* (BUT DON'T THINK THAT NAME IS AN INSULT--THEY ARE *PROUD* OF THEIR MONSTROSITY!)...

LIKE THE *NIGHT MARES,* WHO FASHION AND SEND DREAMS TO SLEEPERS ALL OVER XANTH...

AND THE *DRAGONS,* LARGE AND SMALL, WHO LOVE NOTHING MORE THAN TO GET PASSERS-BY *STEAMED--* LITERALLY!

AND THE *CENTAURS,* A VERY PROUD RACE INDEED. CENTAURS HAVE BEEN HEROES THROUGHOUT THE HISTORY OF XANTH, AND *CENTAUR ISLE* IS A CENTAUR--ER, CENTER OF LEARNING.

CHEIRON AND *CHEX CENTAUR* ARE AN EVEN NEWER BREED OF STEED, AS THEY HAVE WINGS AND CAN FLY. THEY ALSO HAVE A SON, *CHE,* WHOM THEY LOVE DEARLY.

EXCEPT...

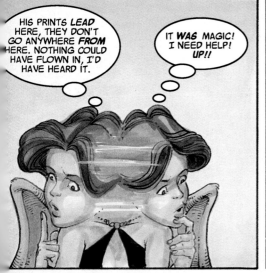

IT IS NOT A SHORT TRIP TO THE PLACE WHERE THE RULERS - THE **MAGICIANS** - OF XANTH HAVE LIVED FOR CENTURIES...

THE JOURNEY TAKES **CHEX CENTAUR** OVER FOREST AND MARSH, AND ACROSS THE GREAT **GAP CHASM** THAT SPLITS XANTH IN TWO...

BUT SHE IS DRIVEN BY A MOTHER'S FIERCE LOVE AND DEEP FEAR. HER FOAL -- ALL OF FIVE YEARS OLD -- IS GONE. AND IT WAS MAGIC THAT TOOK HIM.

ELECTRA!

CHEX!!!

...EVERYBODY!

≥ AHEM! ≤

WE MUST COVER AS MUCH OF XANTH AS QUICKLY AS POSSIBLE. IT'S NOT SAFE TO BE ALONE IN THE WOODS-- OGRES EXCEPTED, OF COURSE-- SO ALL SEARCH PARTIES WILL CONSIST OF TWO OR MORE FOLK!

THESE ARE MAGIC WHISTLES FROM THE CASTLE ARMORY. EVERY PERSON MUST CARRY ONE TO WARN OF DANGER. THEY CAN BE HEARD FAR AND WIDE.

ME BLOW, HEAR NO!

THAT'S BECAUSE YOU AREN'T FAR AND WIDE YET. WE'RE STANDING TOO CLOSE AND NARROW.

OH...

I'M TO GO WITH YOU. MURPHY FIGURES IT'D BE GOOD TO HAVE SOMEONE WITH YOU WHO CAN TALK TO ANYBODY--EVEN THE PLANTS!

THEN WE TAKE OUR LEAVE NOW!

"AND THEN *CHE* -- BEAUTIFUL CHE -- ARRIVED. LIFE WAS SO GOOD, WE WERE SO HAPPY..."

"WE NEVER LACKED FOR FOAL SITTERS WHENEVER WE HAD TO GO SOMEWHERE. NO ONE COULD WANT TO HURT *CHE*... UNLESS..."

"MAYBE IT'S CHE'S *DEATH* THAT SETS OFF A RAMPAGE OF ALL THE WINGED MONSTERS -- *THAT* WOULD CERTAINLY WREAK CHANGE!"

"*NO!* I WON'T ACCEPT THAT! NO ONE WANTS IT -- NOT EVEN THE NON-FLYING DRAGONS. THEY'RE NOT EVEN BOUND BY THE SIMURGH'S OATH, AND THEY *STILL* WATCH OUT FOR CHE!"

"SO WHO..?"

UM, THERE'S SOMETHING DOWN THERE YOU MIGHT WANT TO TAKE A LOOK AT...

≳ GASP! ≲ GOBLINS!

AND YOU KNOW THEY EAT...

BE *QUIET!!*

NO, WE HAVEN'T SEEN ANYTHING YET -- SORRY.

NO. THERE'S NO FIRE. THE POT IS COLD. THEY CAN'T HAVE...DONE IT SO QUICKLY. WE MUST CHECK THE OTHERS!

AND SO...

YOU'D BETTER BE MORE CAREFUL BEFORE SOMEONE DOWN THERE SEES SOMETHING HE SHOULDN'T!

NADA AND ELECTRA... THEY'RE ON THEIR WAY TO THE GOOD MAGICIAN'S CASTLE...IF ANYONE KNOWS ANYTHING IT'LL BE HIM -- BUT IT'LL COST A YEAR OF SERVITUDE TO GET THE ANSWER.

'LECTRA, MAYBE THE MAGICIAN HAS AN ANSWER TO OUR PROBLEM, TOO. IT'LL ONLY COST A YEAR.

YOU KNOW, DOLPH KNOWS, EVERYONE KNOWS I DON'T HAVE A YEAR. I HAVE A WEEK. AND THEN...WELL, YOU KNOW THAT TOO.

OOPS, I DON'T DARE GO IN THERE. AH WELL, DOLPH OUGHT TO BE ALL RIGHT -- WHICHEVER OF THE ELEMENTS HE HAS TO SEARCH, HE CAN CHANGE INTO SOMETHING TO SURVIVE IT -- FIRE, WATER, WHATEVER.

I'D BETTER GET BACK TO OUR STABLE IN CASE NEWS HAS COME THERE.

WHAT'S THAT?! SOMEONE SNOOPING!

EE-YIPE!!

WHAT ARE YOU?!?!

MEANWHILE...

I WISH HE'D JUST MARRY *YOU*, 'LECTRA.

SNAP

SNAP

YOU KNOW THERE'S NO CHANCE OF THAT, WITH YOU SO... AND ME SO... AND ESPECIALLY *PRINCE DOLPH* SO...

"IT WASN'T MY FAULT I GOT SPELLED INTO SLEEPING ALL THOSE CENTURIES, OR THAT I'D LOVE THE PRINCE WHO WOKE ME, OR THAT I'D HAVE TO MARRY HIM BY MY EIGHTEENTH REAL BIRTHDAY NEXT WEEK -- OR DIE..."

"AND IT'S NOT *YOUR* FAULT HE LOVES YOU, BECAUSE YOU'RE SO PRETTY, BUT YOU DON'T LOVE HIM, AND HE DOESN'T LOVE ME, AND HE WANTS TO MARRY YOU, AND IF HE DOESN'T MARRY ME..."

'LECTRA...

WHAT?

HE'S FIFTEEN. HE'S DUMB.

OH... ≶GIGGLE≶ YEAH.

WE'LL FIND A WAY.

OK.

UH-OH. WE'RE GOING TO HAVE TO WORK FOR OUR ANSWERS!

I SAID, WE WANT TO KNOW WHERE *CHE CENTAUR* IS. HE'S BEEN FOAL-NAPPED AND WE THOUGHT TO TRY HERE WHILE THE OTHERS ARE SEARCHING. IT'S PRETTY URGENT.

OH NO... THIS IS ALL WRONG!

YOU SEE, I WAS CERTAIN THAT YOU WERE COMING HERE TO INQUIRE ABOUT YOUR PROBLEM WITH *PRINCE DOLPH!* OH DEAR!

I'VE JUST SPENT I DON'T KNOW *HOW* LONG ON THAT QUESTION. OH DEAR, OH DEAR! AND IT WILL TAKE TIME TO RESEARCH THIS NEW ANSWER.

MAYBE THE MIRROR..?

HMM, PERHAPS. T IT IS FINICKY. I'LL E TO ASK IN RHYME.

MIRROR, MIRROR FROM MY DESK NDULGE ME NOW WITHOUT BURLESQUE IS *CHE CENTAUR* PICTURESQUE?

I FIND THE QUERY MOST GROTESQUE.

"HOWEVER..."

OH NO!! HE'S BEEN CAPTURED BY GOBLINS!

THIS MIGHT HAVE HAPPENED HOURS AGO -- WE STILL DON'T KNOW IF HE'S ALIVE *NOW*. AND WE DON'T KNOW WHICH TRIBE THESE GOBS BELONG TO. I'LL HAVE TO TRY *GHORGE*.

GHORGE?

THE GHOST WRITER. HE COULD FIND *CHE* IN A FLASH AND WRITE US IF THE CHILD IS STILL ALL RIGHT -- BUT HE HATES GOBLINS. THEY'RE THE ONES WHO KILLED AND ATE HIM... HE MAY NOT WANT TO HELP.

WE'LL SEE ABOUT THAT...

WE REALLY NEED TO KNOW WHERE AND HOW CHE IS... WON'T YOU *PLEASE* HELP?

??

AND SO...

Go find Che with a Cookie!

BUT WHAT KIND OF COOKIE DO WE FIND HIM WITH?

NO -- HE MEANS THAT *CHE* IS STILL ALIVE AND HE'S TO BE FOUND SOMEWHERE ALONG THE *WITH-A-COOKIE RIVER!*

AND I KNOW JUST THE THING TO GET YOU THERE AS FAST AS POSSIBLE! YOU'LL HAVE TO BE CAREFUL OF TRAPS, AND TAKE CARE NOT TO LOSE YOUR SOULS, BUT THE TRIP WILL TAKE NO TIME AT ALL!

THE *HYPNO-GOURD,* REALM OF DREAMS!

STEP IN AND YOU'RE ON YOUR WAY!

MEANWHILE, BACK AT OUR ORIGINAL CHEX POINT...

YOU'RE NOT FROM AROUND HERE, ARE YOU?

I DON'T EVEN KNOW WHERE "HERE" IS! EVERYTHING IS ALL BLURRY!

"BLURRY?"

MAYBE *THIS* IS WHAT YOU NEED! WE'LL MAKE A SPECTACLE OF YOU YET!

WHAT..?

OH! THIS IS WONDERFUL! WHAT *ARE* THESE?

THEY'RE FROM THE SPECTACLE BUSH. THIS IS *XANTH,* WHERE *EVERYTHING* HAS MAGIC!

SHOES GROW ON SHOE-TREES, LOAVES OF BREAD ON BREADFRUIT PLANTS... AND I AM *CHEX CENTAUR.*

MY NAME IS *JENNY* AND I'M AN ELF FROM THE *WORLD OF TWO MOONS.*

SOME OF THE ELVES HAVE SOME MAGIC POWERS, BUT THAT'S ALL... AND THERE'S *NO ONE* LIKE YOU THERE!

"SAMMY-- THAT'S MY CAT -- AND I WERE PLAYING, AND I SAID I WISHED I HAD A FEATHER TO TICKLE HIM... WELL, HE CAN FIND ANYTHING SO HE TOOK OFF LIKE AN ARROW..."

"HE WON'T STOP UNTIL HE FINDS WHAT HE'S BEEN ASKED TO... SO WE RAN AND RAN AND WENT INTO A CLOUD I'D NEVER SEEN BEFORE..."

"AND THEN ALL OF A SUDDEN, WE WERE HERE!"

AND I DON'T HAVE ANY IDEA HOW TO GET BACK.

THIS IS A DAY FOR PROBLEMS. YOU'RE AN ELF WHO'S NOT AN ELF WHO'S LOST, AND YOUR SAMMYCAT HAS FOUND ALL THAT'S LEFT OF MY POOR FOAL, CHE...

JENNYELF, MAYBE YOU DON'T HAVE THE SAME MAGIC AS XANTH FOLK...

...BUT PLEASE HELP ME FIND CHE!

I'M SORRY, CHEX... I JUST NEVER HAD ANY MAGIC THAT ANYONE COULD TELL... BUT MAYBE SAMMY COULD..?

...FIND..?

SAMMY!! WAIT FOR ME!

HERE GOES!

EXPLODING CHERRIES?!?! AT LEAST THE NASTY MEN ARE GONE -- I'D BETTER HURRY!

...ON'T BE AFRAID. ...JENNY ELF AND I'M HERE TO HELP YOU!

I AM HAPPY TO MEET YOU...THOSE GOBLINS HAD PLANS FOR ME THAT... WELL, WE'D BETTER GO FAST FROM HERE!

YOU'RE RIGHT. THEY'LL BE BACK SOON. CAN YOU RUN?

YES, I THINK SO. I...

...IIIIEEEE!!

SO! WHAT'S GOING ON HERE?

AN ELF?! HELPING ONE OF THE WINGED MONSTERS?? UNHEARD OF! WHAT PLOT IS THIS??

I GUESS SHE THINKS I'M A XANTH ELF...

THEY'RE ALLIED WITH THE GOBLINS. THAT'S *GODIVA GOBLIN*, AND AS LONG AS SHE'S GOT THAT WAND, WE'RE STUCK!

BUT AT THAT MOMENT...

NO!!

OOOFF!!

SAMMY! RUN! FIND A SAFE PLACE! CHE!! LET'S *GO*!

GOOD SAMMY!

THE GOBLINS WON'T FOLLOW US INTO THE RIVER -- THE WATER MOCCASINS WOULD GET THEM!

OH HO! WHAT FUN CAN I HAVE WITH THIS?

≷GASP≷ IT'S *FRACTO!* HE HATES EVERYTHING AND EVERY-ONE! SWIM, JENNY ELF, FOR YOUR LIFE!

≷SPUTTER!≷

≷COUGH!≷

OH NO! NOT AGAIN!

...CAN'T SHAKE THIS THING!

WAIT A MINUTE! I'M A *GHOST!* WHATEVER IT IS, IT *CAN'T* HURT ME!

WHAAT DOOO YOUUU WAAANT?

YOU ARE AN INTRUDER HERE! WHO ARE YOU?

!!!

I AM *PRINCE DOLPH* OF THE HUMAN FOLK AND I'M ON URGENT BUSINESS. CHE CENTAUR IS MISSING AND I MUST HELP FIND HIM!

WHO ARE YOU?

OH, WELL THEN, I CAN SAVE YOU THE TROUBLE. YOUR LITTLE FOAL ISN'T HERE AT ALL...

AND I...

...AM THE DEMONESS *METRIA,* AND NOW THAT I KNOW YOU'RE REALLY A LIVING MAN, I CAN THINK OF MUCH MORE INTERESTING THINGS TO OCCUPY YOUR TIME....

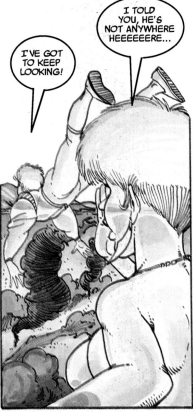

NADA! YOU'RE HERE! BUT HOW..?

NEVER MIND ELECTRA. MARRY *ME*. I'LL SHOW YOU THINGS YOU'VE ONLY DREAMED OF...

N-NO...I DON'T WANT 'LECTRA TO DIE...N-NADA?

THEN MARRY *ME*, DOLPH. I LOVE YOU! NADA'LL GET OVER IT.

YOU'RE THE DEMON LADY! I WON'T FALL FOR ANY MORE OF YOUR TRICKS!

I ADMIT I'M IMPRESSED -- YOU RESISTED ME. AS A REWARD, I'LL TELL YOU THE TRUTH. *BOTH* THREATS ARE REAL -- THE HOLE IN XANTH AND CHE'S FOALNAPPING -- AND BOTH ARE GRAVE!

SO YOU *STILL* HAVE TO CHOOSE. CHE IS FAR AWAY, THE RIP IS CLOSER. THE GOBLINS MIGHT NOT COOK CHE FOR A WHILE, BUT... AND NOTHING MIGHT COME THROUGH THE GAP -- OR SOMETHING HORRIBLE COULD BE THERE NOW.

I'VE MADE UP MY MIND. LET'S GO SEE THIS HOLE OF YOURS.

≶SNICKER≷ MAYBE YOU KNOW MORE ABOUT THE STORK THAN YOU THINK! HAHA!

WHAT'D I SAY?

AND BACK WHERE EVERYTHING BEGAN...

YOU WANT TO TELL ME WHAT THAT WAS ALL ABOUT?

AT THIS POINT, I DON'T KNOW ANY MORE WHAT'S WHERE OR WHO'S WHAT!

OH! *GHORGE!* HELLO TO YOU TOO. JUST A MOMENT AND I'LL FIND YOU SOME PAPER.

CHE CAPTURED BY GOBLINS AT WITH-A-COOKIE RIVER... NADA AND ELECTRA ON THEIR WAY TO HELP!

THEN WE SHOULD ALERT ALL THE OTHER SEARCHERS -- *GRUNDY*, YOU TAKE CARE OF THE ANIMALS AND PLANTS.

THANKS, GHORGE, YOU'VE BEEN A GREAT HELP!

Da Nada

HUH??

WHY HAVE YOU INVADED MY RETREAT, UNANNOUNCED, UNWANTED...

...FAR OUT OF BOUNDS OF YOUR OWN PASTURE?

WE APOLOGIZE -- IT IS VITAL I GET BACK TO MY MATE *CHEIRON,* WHO IS AT A CONFERENCE OF THE WINGED MONSTERS...

BUT *FRACTO* IS MAKING TROUBLE AND WON'T LET US THROUGH!

THEN IT IS NOT YOUR FAULT. WE HAVE NO LOVE FOR THE CLOUD-DEMON EITHER, FOR EVEN THOUGH HE HAS LITTLE POWER THIS HIGH UP, HE STILL RAINS ON US NOW AND THEN...

AND THE MOON IS SUPPOSED TO BE DRY!

IT'S NOT FAIR! IF ONLY THERE WERE SOME WAY TO GIVE *HIM* A BAD DREAM!

IT HAS NEVER BEEN TRIED, BUT THERE IS NO REASON IT COULDN'T WORK. I WILL ASK...

AND MOMENTS LATER...

BEHOLD, THE *NIGHT STALLION!*

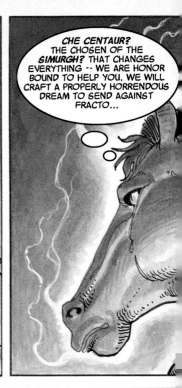

THE WAY IS CLEAR NOW. THANKS.

GOOD LUCK!

THERE IT IS -- MOUNT RUSHMOST. OH, I HOPE HE'S STILL THERE.

"I HOPE MY CHEIRON IS STILL THERE..."

THERE, THERE...

THIS IS DISTURBING NEWS THAT CHEX BRINGS, AND IT IS NOT ONLY PERSONAL. NO, ITS IMPLICATIONS ARE FAR MORE DIRE THAN THAT. THE GOBLINS, CREATURES OF THE LAND, HAVE STOLEN MY SON, WHO IS OF THE AIR. I AM AFRAID, MY FRIENDS AND KIN, THAT WE AND XANTH FACE WHAT NO ONE HAS SEEN FOR CENTURIES...

WE FACE WAR.

AND WHAT OF THE OBJECT OF THAT WAR?

THESE DON'T LOOK LIKE THE SAME GOBLINS WE RAN AWAY FROM.

THEY ARE NOT. AND I FEAR THEY ARE MUCH WORSE.

HOW COULD THEY BE WORSE?

GODIVA DID NOT TREAT ME BADLY -- AND IF THESE ARE WHO I THINK...

NO TALKING!

AT LEAST WE HAVE MOONLIGHT SO WE CAN SEE TO WALK... HEY, WHERE'S THE OTHER MOON?

THERE IS ONLY ONE. WHY?

I REALLY AND TRULY AM ON ANOTHER WORLD!

OOOHH!!

HEY! YO CLUMSY..

GO! GO FETCH OUR EVENING SPORT!

≈GIGGLE!≈

≈SCHNORT!≈

≈CHUCKLE!≈

HEEHEE! NOW THEY HAVE TO CHASE EACH OTHER. IF SHE CATCHES HIM FIRST, SHE GOES FREE AND WE COOK THE FAUN.

IF HE CATCHES HER, IT'S THE REVERSE. IF THEY REFUSE TO RUN, WE BOIL THEM BOTH!

GO!!

ENOUGH FOOLISHNESS! MAKE THEM RUN!!

WHY DON'T THEY JUST ESCAPE INTO THE WATER? THEY COULD SWIM TO THE OTHER SIDE AND BE FREE!

"I DON'T KNOW -- THERE MUST BE SOMETHING ABOUT THAT WATER..."

"THEY SEEM MORE AFRAID OF GETTING WET THAN OF THE GOBLINS OR THEIR COOK-POT!"

"JENNY! I UNDERSTAND NOW! IT'S A HATE-POOL! WHATEVER SOMEONE FEELS BEFORE..."

ARRRRRHH!!

MMMMMMM...

IN THERE WITH YOU! AND THINK ABOUT WHAT YOU'VE SEEN! HA!

AT LEAST WE'RE NOT TIED UP ANY MORE.

CHE -- I'M SCARED!

THE GOBLINS DON'T HAVE TO WORRY ABOUT US -- THIS HUT IS BARRED FROM THE OUTSIDE.

I'M WORRIED TOO, JENNY-ELF, BUT I AM TIRED EVEN MORE. LET'S TRY TO REST... AND HAVE HOPE...

I WONDER..?

BACK HOME I COULD "SEND" AND CALL HELP! MAYBE..?

*

PUCKERNUTS! NO ONE CAN HEAR ME!

AT LEAST I CAN STILL SING -- THAT ALWAYS MAKES ME FEEL BETTER.

♪♪♪

♪♩♫♪

EVEN IN THE FACE OF TERROR, JENNY'S SINGING CONJURES PLEASANT REVERIE FOR HER.

THAT IS VERY NICE!

OH!! I DIDN'T KNOW YOU WERE LISTENING!

I HAD THE MOST PLEASANT DREAM... OF A PRINCE AND A PRINCESS...

THAT'S THE DAYDREAM *I* HAD AS I WAS SINGING!

DO YOU SUPPOSE MY "SENDING" MAGIC WORKS DIFFERENT HERE? THAT MAYBE I CAN MAKE PEOPLE HAVE DREAMS WHEN I SING?

PERHAPS YOU CAN TRY IT ON THE GOBL...

...INS...

HERE!!

IT'S ALL YOU'LL GET, SO EAT IT! NOW! BECAUSE IF YOU DON'T, YOU'RE *NEXT* IN THE POT!

"NEXT"? OH, CHE! THAT'S...

I'M AFRAID SO.

OH *NO*..!

I DON'T UNDERSTAND YOU! SUDDENLY, WITHOUT THINKING, YOU'RE DOING THE RIGHT THING!

OF COURSE YOU DON'T UNDERSTAND -- YOU'RE NOT HUMAN. NOW ARE YOU GOING TO STOP DISTRACTING ME AND HELP, OR NOT?

HMM. THIS COULE BECOME THE DAY OF THE DOLPH YET!

OGRES DON'T FEAR ANYTHING -- MAYBE IF I...

LET'S GET THAT THING!!

>GULP!< LET'S TRY...

NO... GOOD..! CAN'T... MOVE...!

AGGGKK!!

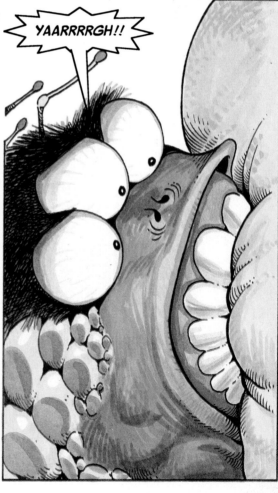

AH HA! GINGER SNAPS! THIS MUST BE THE WITH-A-COOKIE!

SKRAWWK! OUT OF HERE, YOU WHIPPERSNAPPER!

BUT WHERE CAN THEY BE? IT'S A LONG RIVER! AND I SURE CAN'T FLY THE WHOLE LENGTH WITH ALL THESE TREES OVERHANGING EVERYTHING.

I NEED THE PROPER SHAPE...

A HARPIE?! GET OUT OF HERE BEFORE YOU POISON THE WATER!

IS THAT SO, STINK-FACED SON OF A WOMAN?

LET'S SEE HOW *YOUR* FACE LIKES *THIS*!

A FEEBLE THREAT, PRINCE! I'LL BURY YOU IN SPIT!

"PRINCE"? I NEVER MENTIONED I WAS A PRINCE TO THIS HAR...

METRIA!!

AND JUST WHAT DO YOU THINK YOU'RE DOING?

I'M TRYING TO DETERMINE IF THIS CAT IS YOU IN DISGUISE... ERR...

DUMB! WHAT DOES THIS CAT WANT?

HE SAYS "HELP"...

TO GIVE IT OR GET IT?

<JENNY ELF SAID FIND HELP. I FOUND YOU>

<SO YOU FIND THINGS? CAN YOU FIND ANYTHING?>

<YES>

<HOW..?>

DUMB! DUMBER! ASK HIM TO FIND WHAT YOU WANT!

ALL RIGHT, SAMMY, IF YOU CAN FIND ANYTHING AT ALL, FIND NADA NAGA!

AFTER HIM!

I'LL MAKE MUCH BETTER TIME BY TAKING THE SERPENT TEEN PATH!

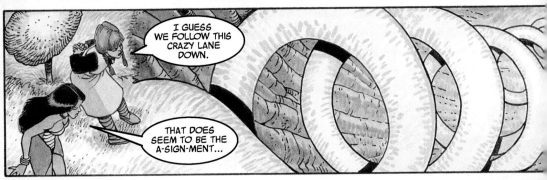

OH *ELECTRA!* YOU SHOULDN'T HAVE DONE THAT! I THOUGHT I SAW SOME- ONE ATTACKING -- I DIDN'T WANT US BOTH TO DIE!

B-BUT... YOU WERE IN DANGER! I COULDN'T...

HUSH... I WAS ONLY THINKING OF YOU. AND WITH ME GONE, IT WOULD CERTAINLY SOLVE THE PROBLEM WITH DOLPH.

WHAT?!? WHAT DO YOU...

??? SLOWING?

NEVER MIND NOW -- OUR FALL IS SLOWING -- WE'RE GOING TO BE ALL RIGHT...

A LITTLE LATER...

AH! I'VE FOUND THE PATH FIRST. IF I HIDE AND WAIT THE SIGN WON'T DISAPPEAR AND ELECTRA WILL *HAVE* TO COME THIS WAY EVENTUALLY!

AND SURE ENOUGH...

OH GOOD! THE PATH! I'LL RUN AND CATCH UP WITH NADA!

IT'S WORKING! SHE'LL ESCAPE THE GOURD AND I'LL...

I'LL WHAT? NOW *I'M* LOST IN HERE!

AH WELL. IT'S WHAT I WANTED FOR 'LECTRA. SHE'LL GET OUT AND DOLPH WILL HAVE TO MARRY HER -- HE'LL LEARN TO LIKE IT.

AND MAYBE I CAN FIND A JOB IN HERE -- WORKING FOR THE NIGHT STALLION, PERHAPS...

THIS MUST BE *CROSS CITY!*

THEN *THESE* ARE ALL CROSSROA...

NADA!!

WHERE CHE *WAS*, I THINK. IT'S TOO QUIET AND STILL HERE NOW.

CAN YOU USE YOUR SNAKE SENSES TO TRACK HIM?

≷SNIF≷ WELL, HE WAS DEFINITELY HERE ≷SNIF≷ JUST A LITTLE WHILE AGO ≷SNIF≷

≷SNIF≷ DO YOU KNOW IF THERE ARE ANY *ELF ELMS* NEAR HERE?

COULD BE. WHY?

I'M SCENTING AN ELF, BUT DIFFERENT FROM ANY XANTH ELF I KNOW...

ANYWAY, WE'VE GOT TO GET GOING. IF YOU CARRY ME IN YOUR BODICE I CAN GUIDE YOU.

LOOK! THERE'S LIGHT UP AHEAD!

QUIETLY NOW...

FIRST, WE'RE NOT THE ONES WHO HAVE THE FOAL.

WE'RE TRYING TO RESCUE HIM OURSELVES FROM THE *GOLDEN HORDE* GOBLINS BEFORE THEY BOIL AND EAT HIM.

"WE ARE FROM *GOBLIN MOUNTAIN* TO THE FAR EAST -- MY MOTHER, *GOLDY GOBLIN,* GOT THE MAGIC WAND FROM AN OGRE WHO WAS PASSING THROUGH..."

"SHE USED ITS POWER TO SNARE THE SON OF THE GOBLIN CHIEF..."

"...AND IN DUE TIME THEY SUMMONED THE STORK AND I ARRIVED."

"I USED THE WAND MYSELF AND SNAGGED A MATE, AND FOR US THE STORK DELIVERED MY DAUGHTER *GWENDOLYN*..."

"WHO WAS AS LOVELY AS ANY FEMALE CHILD COULD BE."

"BUT THROUGH A TRAGIC MISCHANCE SHE WAS MADE LAME AND CAN WALK ONLY WITH DIFFICULTY."

I WON'T HAVE MY DAUGHTER HUMBLED BY CIRCUMSTANCE, SO I DECIDED TO FIND A STEED FOR HER TO RIDE.

BUT CHE'S TOO YOUNG TO RIDE -- AND HIS PARENTS ARE GOING CRAZY MISSING HIM!

IT'S A MOOT POINT NOW, ANY-WAY...

...SINCE THAT *ELF* SPOOKED MY TROOPS WITH HER CHERRY BOMBS AND MADE OFF WITH THE FOAL.

WHO *IS* THAT ELF??

IT'S A MYSTERY. APPARENTLY THEY ARE ALLIES... BUT THE MAIN THING NOW IS TO RESCUE THE FOAL BEFORE HE IS KILLED.

WE CAN DECIDE HIS DISPOSITION LATER.

I HAVE MAGICAL POWER IN THIS WAND -- THE FOAL KNOWS YOU TWO AS FRIENDS -- WE EACH HAVE SOMETHING THE OTHERS CAN USE. WE *MUST* HELP EACH OTHER!

ALL RIGHT. I DON'T LIKE IT, BUT YOU HAVE A POINT, AND YOU'VE BEEN FAIR. WE WILL WORK TOGETHER TO RESCUE CHE.

BUT WHATEVER OUR AGREEMENT LATER, THE WINGED MONSTERS WILL WANT HIM BACK. BE WARNED, GODIVA.

...OUTSIDE AND GET READY TO RUN!

I CAN CHANGE TO A GIANT SERPENT AND GO IN...

BUT YOU'LL ROUSE THE ENTIRE CAMP -- THERE ARE DOZENS OF THEM!

THERE'S NO SINGLE GOOD PLAN! YOU CAN ONLY LIFT ONE THING AT A TIME; I CAN ONLY DEAL WITH A COUPLE OF GOBLINS AT ONCE... WE'VE JUST TO DO OUR BEST AND COUNT ON SURPRISE!

IT'LL BE UP TO YOU TO GET CHE OUT ONCE THE DUST STARTS FLYING. YOU GET HIM TO SAFETY, NO MATTER WHAT HAPPENS TO ME. PROMISE?

NADA... OH... OK. I PROMISE.

GET READY -- I'LL DISTRACT 'EM GOOD!